For Eve, Emma & Poppy

First published in Great Britain in 2011 by Nancy Rose Publications.

Printed in Great Britain by Reeds Printers.

Text and illustrations Copyright © Nancy Rose Publications 2011

ISBN 978-0-9568340-0-3

The author/illustrator asserts the moral rights to be identified
as the author/illustrator of the work.

A CIP catalogue record for this book is available from the British Library.

www.skippthesailor.com

Skipp Goes Sailing

Nancy Rose

Skipp the Sailor was feeling adventurous!

He had already explored the boat yard
and now he wanted a new challenge.

The sun was shining and the wind was blowing
– it was the perfect weather for sailing!

So, he went to see his friend Cranky Colin,
the crane, who lived around the corner
on the other side of the boat yard.

"Hello Cranky Col!" said Skipp. "Would you like to go for a sail on Windy Waters today?

The sun is shining and the wind is blowing – it's the perfect weather for sailing!"

"I'm sorry Skipp, I can't go sailing today," replied Cranky Col. "I'm a crane you see, and cranes don't float. I'm afraid I would sink," he said grumpily. "Why don't you ask somebody else?"

"Okay," said Skipp and off he went.

Skipp carried on, past the boat yard and down towards the edge of the lake.

All of a sudden he heard a loud "WOOF, WOOF!" and Millie and Lottie came running out of the lake.

They bounded up to Skipp, dripping water as they ran. When they reached Skipp, they shook the water out of their fur and all over him!

"Hello Millie! Hello Lottie!" said Skipp.

"The sun is shining and the wind is blowing –
it's the perfect weather for sailing!
Would you like to go sailing with me?"

"We've already been in the lake today
and now we're tired. Perhaps we could go
tomorrow?" said the dogs and off they ran
with their wet tails wagging.

Skipp went back to the boat yard to look for James, the boat yard boy.

"Hi James," said Skipp.
"Would you like to come sailing with me?

The sun is shining and the wind is blowing – it's the perfect weather for sailing!"

"I'm afraid I have lots of work to do at the moment Skipp, so we'll have to go another time."

"That's okay" said Skipp, feeling sad at the thought of not going sailing after all.

"Wait a minute Skipp", shouted James.
"Why don't you go down to the jetty and ask
Speedy the rescue boat? I'm sure he would love
to go sailing on Windy Waters."

"That's a great idea!" said Skipp and off he went, running as fast as he could, down to the lakeside jetty where Speedy lived.

"Hi Speedy!" said Skipp excitedly.
He was nearly out of breath, having run so fast.

"The sun is shining and the wind is blowing – it's the perfect weather for sailing! Would you like to go sailing with me?"

"Hello there Skipp!"
said Speedy in his bellowing, boisterous voice.

"Unfortunately, I can't. I am a rescue boat you see,
and I have a big, roaring engine but no sails. I must
stay here today in case anyone needs my help."

Skipp felt very disappointed. He was ready to give up and go home.

Then Speedy had an idea. He suggested that Skipp should ask Sloop, the sailing boat, if he would like to go sailing.

"What a brilliant idea!" said Skipp and off he ran along the path, around the edge of Windy Waters Lake and on towards Sloop's mooring at the next jetty.

He raced past the sailing club, past Millie and Lottie and past the boat yard.

Skipp screeched to a halt at Sloop's jetty.

"Hi Sloop!" said Skipp excitedly. "Would you like to go sailing with me today?"

"Hmm, well ...

... of course I would Skipp. I'd love to go!

The sun is shining and the wind is blowing –
it's the perfect weather for sailing!"

...and off they sailed!